Presented to:

_____

By:

_____

Date:

_____

AN EXPECTANT MOTHER'S
Journal

Prompted by
Angela Thomas Guffey

Honor Books
Colorado Springs, Colorado 80918

An Expectant Mother's Journal
ISBN 1-56292-868-6
Copyright © 2001 by Angela Thomas Guffey

Published by Honor Books
4050 Lee Vance View
Colorado Springs, CO 80918

A LETTER FROM ANGELA
(Introduction)

Dear Expectant Mothers,

I am writing to you today from the other side of "expecting." My husband and I are now walking through the sweet days of snuggles and the busy days of homework with our four young children. Motherhood is precious to me, and I am making every effort to savor the tenderness of each moment. And yet, I look into their eyes and know that time is passing all too quickly.

One of the things I am learning in these years is that as the mother, I am the keeper of the memories. My children ask me roughly a million questions a day, and many of these are memory questions—things like: "How did it feel when I was in your tummy?" "What other names did you think about for me?" "What happened on the day I was born?"

That's why journaling during your pregnancy is so important. It's a gift you can give yourself and your children. To write from your heart is to care for your soul during this season of amazing change. And to record the details of these months is to bind up the memories of your anticipation and longing. This journal will become a priceless treasure that you and your child can share together as well as an heirloom that can be passed down one day.

I send you my deepest congratulations along with a twinge of desire . . . there are moments when I wish I were an expectant mother again. Hold each day in your heart, and then record it here in this journal. May you know that you have been covered with the lavish grace of God, may you rest in the peace that He provides, and may you anticipate with great gladness the gift that is growing inside you.

Because of God's Mercy,

Angela Thomas Guffey

EXPECTANT MOTHER'S *Journal*

Was your pregnancy a surprise, or did it take several months of "trying" and waiting? Recount your feelings and thoughts during those days.

_____

_____

_____

_____

_____

_____

_____

_____

_____

_____

_____

_____

_____

_____

_____

_____

_____

_____

_____

_____

_____

_____

_____

_____

_____

_____

In the morning, O LORD, you hear my voice; in the morning
I lay my requests before you and wait in expectation.

Psalm 5:3

EXPECTANT MOTHER'S *Journal*

Recall the very first moment you knew you were pregnant.
How did you tell your husband?

Praise the LORD, O my soul; all my inmost being, praise his holy name.

Psalm 103:1

EXPECTANT MOTHER'S *Journal*

Describe your feelings about the child being formed within you.

_____

_____

_____

_____

_____

_____

_____

_____

_____

_____

_____

_____

_____

_____

_____

_____

_____

_____

_____

_____

_____

_____

_____

_____

"I know the plans I have for you," declares the LORD, "plans to prosper you and not to harm you, plans to give you hope and a future."

Jeremiah 29:11

EXPECTANT MOTHER'S *Journal*

What emotional and physical changes are taking place in your body right now?

_____

_____

_____

_____

_____

_____

_____

_____

_____

_____

_____

_____

_____

_____

_____

_____

_____

_____

_____

_____

_____

_____

_____

"Come to me, all you who are weary and burdened, and
I will give you rest. For my yoke is easy and my burden is light."

Matthew 11:28,30

EXPECTANT MOTHER'S *Journal*

How has the news that you are pregnant impacted your friends
and your family? Do you find any of their responses surprising?

_____

_____

_____

_____

_____

_____

_____

_____

_____

_____

_____

_____

_____

_____

_____

_____

_____

_____

_____

_____

_____

_____

_____

_____

_____

The LORD bless you, and keep you; The LORD make His face shine on you,
And be gracious to you; The LORD lift up His countenance on you,
And give you peace.

Numbers 6:24-26 NASB

EXPECTANT MOTHER'S *Journal*

Describe your first trip to the obstetrician.
What characteristics do you like most about your doctor?

_____

_____

_____

_____

_____

_____

_____

_____

_____

_____

_____

_____

_____

_____

_____

_____

_____

_____

_____

_____

_____

_____

_____

_____

_____

_____

_____

God was kind to the midwives and the people increased and became even more numerous. And because the midwives feared God, he gave them families of their own.

Exodus 1:20-21

EXPECTANT MOTHER'S *Journal*

Are you experiencing any anxious thoughts at this stage of your pregnancy?
Write them down, and then release them to God.

_____

_____

_____

_____

_____

_____

_____

_____

_____

_____

_____

_____

_____

_____

_____

_____

_____

_____

_____

_____

We wait in hope for the LORD; he is our help and our shield. In him
our hearts rejoice, for we trust in his holy name. May your unfailing
love rest upon us, O LORD, even as we put our hope in you.

Psalms 33:20-22

EXPECTANT MOTHER'S *Journal*

Do you feel overly sensitive and tearful? In what ways
do you feel you will most need God's help in the months ahead?

Cast all your anxiety on him because he cares for you.

1 Peter 5:7

EXPECTANT MOTHER'S *Journal*

Assess your current load of responsibilities.
What steps can you take to lighten that load for the season ahead?

_____

_____

_____

_____

_____

_____

_____

_____

_____

_____

_____

_____

_____

_____

_____

_____

_____

_____

_____

_____

_____

_____

_____

The sleep of a laborer is sweet.

Ecclesiastes 5:12

EXPECTANT MOTHER'S *Journal*

Recall specific instances when God has taken care of you in the past.
How will you trust Him during this special time?

"Who of you by worrying can add a single hour to his life? Since you cannot do this very little thing, why do you worry about the rest?"

Luke 12:25-26

EXPECTANT MOTHER'S *Journal*

Describe your husband.
Which of his qualities do you believe will make him a great daddy?

_____

_____

_____

_____

_____

_____

_____

_____

_____

_____

_____

_____

_____

_____

_____

_____

_____

_____

_____

_____

_____

_____

_____

Listen, my sons, to a father's instruction; pay attention and gain understanding.
I give you sound learning, so do not forsake my teaching. When I was a boy
in my father's house, still tender, and an only child of my mother, he taught
me and said, "Lay hold of my words with all your heart; keep my commands
and you will live."

Proverbs 4:1-4

EXPECTANT MOTHER'S *Journal*

Do you have a pregnant friend who has been supportive during this time?
List some ways that you can help and encourage her.

_____

_____

_____

_____

_____

_____

_____

_____

_____

_____

_____

_____

_____

_____

_____

_____

_____

_____

_____

_____

_____

_____

_____

_____

A friend loves at all times.

Proverbs 17:17

EXPECTANT MOTHER'S *Journal*

Recall some of the encouraging comments
people have been saying to you.

"Let your light shine before men, that they may see your good deeds and praise your Father in heaven."

Matthew 5:16

EXPECTANT MOTHER'S *Journal*

How did you feel the first time you heard your baby's heartbeat?
Pause to thank God for the miracle of life.

_____
_____
_____
_____
_____
_____
_____
_____
_____
_____
_____
_____
_____
_____
_____
_____
_____
_____
_____
_____
_____
_____
_____
_____

A joyful heart is good medicine.

Proverbs 17:22 NASB

EXPECTANT MOTHER'S *Journal*

List the new food cravings and aversions
that have come with your pregnancy.
Have any of these created humorous situations?

_____
_____
_____
_____
_____
_____
_____
_____
_____
_____
_____
_____
_____
_____
_____
_____
_____
_____
_____
_____
_____
_____
_____

He who is full loathes honey, but to the hungry even what is bitter tastes sweet.

Proverbs 27:7

EXPECTANT MOTHER'S *Journal*

In what ways can you make your home
a refuge of faith for your children?

_____

_____

_____

_____

_____

_____

_____

_____

_____

_____

_____

_____

_____

_____

_____

_____

_____

_____

_____

_____

_____

_____

_____

_____

As the mountains surround Jerusalem, so the LORD surrounds his people both now and forevermore.

Psalm 125:2

EXPECTANT MOTHER'S *Journal*

What traditions of faith will you pass down to your children?

_____

_____

_____

_____

_____

_____

_____

_____

_____

_____

_____

_____

_____

_____

_____

_____

_____

_____

_____

_____

_____

_____

Point your kids in the right direction—when they're old they won't be lost.

Proverbs 22:6 THE MESSAGE

EXPECTANT MOTHER'S *Journal*

Do people ask, "How many more children are you planning to have?"
If so, how do you respond?

_____

_____

_____

_____

_____

_____

_____

_____

_____

_____

_____

_____

_____

_____

_____

_____

_____

_____

_____

_____

_____

_____

_____

_____

To man belong the plans of the heart, but from the LORD comes the reply
of the tongue.

Proverbs 16:1

EXPECTANT MOTHER'S *Journal*

Describe some of the pregnancy advice you have been given.

_____

_____

_____

_____

_____

_____

_____

_____

_____

_____

_____

_____

_____

_____

_____

_____

_____

_____

_____

_____

_____

_____

_____

Let your conversation be always full of grace, seasoned with salt, so that you may know how to answer everyone.

Colossians 4:6

EXPECTANT MOTHER'S *Journal*

Have you planned your baby's nursery? Close your eyes and imagine it.
Now describe it just as you would like it to be.

_____

_____

_____

_____

_____

_____

_____

_____

_____

_____

_____

_____

_____

_____

_____

_____

_____

_____

_____

_____

_____

Delight yourself in the LORD and he will give you the desires of your heart.

Psalm 37:4

EXPECTANT MOTHER'S *Journal*

Describe the changes taking place in your body.

Hear my cry, O God; listen to my prayer. From the ends of the earth I call to
you, I call as my heart grows faint; lead me to the rock that is higher than I.

Psalms 61:1-2

EXPECTANT MOTHER'S *Journal*

What pressures and frustrations are you feeling right now?

Do everything without complaining or arguing, so that you may become
blameless and pure, children of God.

Philippians 2:14-15

In what areas have you noticed that God is renewing your strength?

_____

_____

_____

_____

_____

_____

_____

_____

_____

_____

_____

_____

_____

_____

_____

_____

_____

_____

_____

_____

_____

_____

The LORD is the everlasting God, the Creator of the ends of the earth.
He will not grow tired or weary, and his understanding no one can fathom.
He gives strength to the weary and increases the power of the weak.

Isaiah 40:28-29

EXPECTANT MOTHER'S *Journal*

What blessings do you believe the birth of this child will bring to your life?

Every good and perfect gift is from above, coming down from the Father of the heavenly lights, who does not change like shifting shadows.

James 1:17

EXPECTANT MOTHER'S *Journal*

What blessings do you believe this child will bring to your husband's life?

_____

_____

_____

_____

_____

_____

_____

_____

_____

_____

_____

_____

_____

_____

_____

_____

_____

_____

_____

_____

_____

_____

Bless the LORD, O my soul, And forget none of His benefits.

Psalm 103:2 NASB

EXPECTANT MOTHER'S *Journal*

What are the three most important principles you will want to pass on to your child?

_____

_____

_____

_____

_____

_____

_____

_____

_____

_____

_____

_____

_____

_____

_____

_____

_____

_____

_____

_____

_____

_____

_____

_____

_____

_____

He commanded our forefathers to teach their children, so the next
generation would know them, even the children yet to be born,
and they in turn would tell their children.

Psalms 78:5-6

EXPECTANT MOTHER'S *Journal*

What parenting style did you learn from your parents? How does it differ from the style your husband learned?

Train up a child in the way he should go,
Even when he is old he will not depart from it.

Proverbs 22:6 NASB

EXPECTANT MOTHER'S *Journal*

What were you doing the first time you felt your baby move?
Describe the sensation and how it made you feel.

As soon as the sound of your greeting reached my ears,
the baby in my womb leaped for joy.

Luke 1:44

EXPECTANT MOTHER'S *Journal*

What birthing options are you considering?
What factors will weigh most heavily in your decision?

God is not a God of confusion but of peace.

1 Corinthians 14:33 NASB

EXPECTANT MOTHER'S *Journal*

What are some names that have been passed down in your family?
What are your choices for a boy? For a girl?

_____

_____

_____

_____

_____

_____

_____

_____

_____

_____

_____

_____

_____

_____

_____

_____

_____

_____

_____

_____

_____

_____

_____

_____

_____

_____

Before I was born the LORD called me; from my birth he has made mention of my name.

Isaiah 49:1

EXPECTANT MOTHER'S *Journal*

Do you wrestle with feelings of inadequacy with regard to mothering?
What steps can you take to overcome those feelings?

_____

_____

_____

_____

_____

_____

_____

_____

_____

_____

_____

_____

_____

_____

_____

_____

_____

_____

_____

_____

_____

_____

_____

_____

Not that we are adequate in ourselves to consider anything
as coming from ourselves, but our adequacy is from God.

2 Corinthians 3:5 NASB

EXPECTANT MOTHER'S *Journal*

Do you plan to work after your child is born?
What are your feelings about this?

Whatever you do, work at it with all your heart,
as working for the Lord, not for men.

Colossians 3:23

EXPECTANT MOTHER'S *Journal*

Describe your best friend.
How has she been there for you during your pregnancy?

Dear friends, let us love one another, for love comes from God.

1 John 4:7

EXPECTANT MOTHER'S *Journal*

What are the strengths your parents will bring to your child's life?
What strengths will your husband's parents bring?

_____

_____

_____

_____

_____

_____

_____

_____

_____

_____

_____

_____

_____

_____

_____

_____

_____

_____

_____

_____

_____

_____

_____

_____

_____

_____

_____

Plans fail for lack of counsel, but with many advisers they succeed.

Proverbs 15:22

EXPECTANT MOTHER'S *Journal*

What are your hopes and dreams for your child's life?
Pause and commit these to God.

_____
_____
_____
_____
_____
_____
_____
_____
_____
_____
_____
_____
_____
_____
_____
_____
_____
_____
_____
_____
_____
_____
_____
_____
_____
_____

"Pray, then, in this way: 'Our Father who is in heaven, Hallowed be Your name.
'Your kingdom come. Your will be done, On earth as it is in heaven.'"

Matthew 6:9-10 NASB

EXPECTANT MOTHER'S *Journal*

Describe your first ultrasound. What were your thoughts and emotions when you saw the image of your unborn child?

_____

_____

_____

_____

_____

_____

_____

_____

_____

_____

_____

_____

_____

_____

_____

_____

_____

_____

_____

_____

_____

_____

_____

_____

_____

Your hands shaped me and made me. . . . You molded me like clay. . . .
Did you not pour me out like milk and curdle me like cheese, clothe me with
skin and flesh and knit me together with bones and sinews? You gave me life
and showed me kindness, and in your providence watched over my spirit.

Job 10:8-12

EXPECTANT MOTHER'S *Journal*

Do you wish to know the sex of your child?
Why do you feel this way?

_____
_____
_____
_____
_____
_____
_____
_____
_____
_____
_____
_____
_____
_____
_____
_____
_____
_____
_____
_____
_____
_____
_____
_____

Behold, thou desirest truth in the inward parts: and in the hidden part thou shalt make me to know wisdom.

Psalm 51:6 KJV

EXPECTANT MOTHER'S *Journal*

Do you wish to nurse your baby?
What are your feelings about nursing?

If any of you lacks wisdom, let him ask of God, who gives to all generously and without reproach, and it will be given to him.

James 1:5 NASB

EXPECTANT MOTHER'S *Journal*

What steps are you taking to care for your soul during pregnancy?
How successful have your efforts been so far?

Those who wait for the LORD Will gain new strength; They will mount up with wings like eagles, They will run and not get tired, They will walk and not become weary.

Isaiah 40:31 NASB

EXPECTANT MOTHER'S *Journal*

Are you sensing God's love for you during these months?
Describe your feelings.

"Though the mountains be shaken and the hills be removed, yet my unfailing love for you will not be shaken nor my covenant of peace be removed," says the LORD, who has compassion on you.

Isaiah 54:10

EXPECTANT MOTHER'S *Journal*

One day your baby will be grown and have a spouse.
What are your thoughts and prayers for
your future son or daughter-in-law?

_____

_____

_____

_____

_____

_____

_____

_____

_____

_____

_____

_____

_____

_____

_____

_____

_____

_____

_____

_____

_____

_____

Commit your way to the LORD, Trust also in Him, And He shall bring it to pass.

Psalm 37:5 NKJV

EXPECTANT MOTHER'S *Journal*

What is the most helpful advice you have been given about labor and delivery?

Commit everything you do to the Lord. Trust him to help you do it and he will.

Psalm 37:5 TLB

EXPECTANT MOTHER'S *Journal*

How has your personal faith impacted your pregnancy?
Describe several specific instances.

_____

_____

_____

_____

_____

_____

_____

_____

_____

_____

_____

_____

_____

_____

_____

_____

_____

_____

_____

_____

_____

_____

_____

_____

_____

_____

_____

Let us then approach the throne of grace with confidence, so that we may receive mercy and find grace to help us in our time of need.

Hebrews 4:16

EXPECTANT MOTHER'S *Journal*

What have your parents told you about your temperament as a child?
What are the traits you hope your child will receive from you?

_____

_____

_____

_____

_____

_____

_____

_____

_____

_____

_____

_____

_____

_____

_____

_____

_____

_____

_____

_____

_____

_____

_____

_____

A cheerful heart brings a smile to your face; a sad heart makes it hard to get through the day.

Proverbs 15:13 THE MESSAGE

EXPECTANT MOTHER'S *Journal*

What have your husband's parents said about his temperament as a child?
What are the traits you hope your child will receive from your husband?

Be made new in the attitude of your minds . . . put on the new self, created to be like God in true righteousness and holiness.

Ephesians 4:23-24

EXPECTANT MOTHER'S *Journal*

What prenatal tests have been suggested by your doctor?
Describe your feelings about these procedures.

_____

_____

_____

_____

_____

_____

_____

_____

_____

_____

_____

_____

_____

_____

_____

_____

_____

_____

_____

_____

_____

_____

_____

_____

_____

"Peace I leave with you; my peace I give you. . . . Do not let your hearts be troubled and do not be afraid."

John 14:27

EXPECTANT MOTHER'S *Journal*

How has your husband been dealing with your pregnancy?
What steps can you take to strengthen and encourage him?

_____

_____

_____

_____

_____

_____

_____

_____

_____

_____

_____

_____

_____

_____

_____

_____

_____

_____

_____

_____

_____

_____

_____

_____

Therefore encourage one another and build each other up, just as in fact you are doing.

1 Thessalonians 5:11

EXPECTANT MOTHER'S *Journal*

How are you feeling about the changes in your personal appearance?
What steps can you take to "perk up" your self-esteem?

_____
_____
_____
_____
_____
_____
_____
_____
_____
_____
_____
_____
_____
_____
_____
_____
_____
_____
_____
_____
_____
_____
_____
_____
_____
_____

I have learned in whatever state I am, to be content.

Philippians 4:11 NKJV

EXPECTANT MOTHER'S *Journal*

What "baby stuff" do you still need for your child's arrival?
What will you and your baby wear home from the hospital?

_____

_____

_____

_____

_____

_____

_____

_____

_____

_____

_____

_____

_____

_____

_____

_____

_____

_____

_____

_____

_____

_____

_____

_____

"Your Father knows what you need before you ask Him."

Matthew 6:8 NASB

EXPECTANT MOTHER'S *Journal*

Describe your favorite and most comfy maternity clothes.
Will you keep them or pass them along to another expectant mother?

_____
_____
_____
_____
_____
_____
_____
_____
_____
_____
_____
_____
_____
_____
_____
_____
_____
_____
_____
_____
_____
_____
_____
_____
_____

Good will come to him who is generous and lends freely, who conducts his affairs with justice.

Psalm 112:5

EXPECTANT MOTHER'S *Journal*

Describe the kind deeds done by neighbors and friends
during your pregnancy. Pause and thank God for them.

As each one has received a gift, minister it to one another, as good stewards
of the manifold grace of God.

EXPECTANT MOTHER'S *Journal*

Do you have an older woman in your life
whom you can look to for wisdom and direction?
What qualities would make her a good "mommy mentor"?

Teach the older women to be reverent in the way they live. . . . Then they can train the younger women to love their husbands and children.

EXPECTANT MOTHER'S *Journal*

How is your husband taking special care of you during this time?
How are you taking special care of him?

_____

_____

_____

_____

_____

_____

_____

_____

_____

_____

_____

_____

_____

_____

_____

_____

_____

_____

_____

_____

_____

_____

_____

_____

The wife does not have authority over her own body, but the husband does; and likewise also the husband does not have authority over his own body, but the wife does.

1 Corinthians 7:4 NASB

EXPECTANT MOTHER'S *Journal*

Describe the house your baby will come home to.
What is your favorite room?

_____
_____
_____
_____
_____
_____
_____
_____
_____
_____
_____
_____
_____
_____
_____
_____
_____
_____
_____
_____
_____
_____
_____
_____
_____

By wisdom a house is built, and through understanding it is established;
through knowledge its rooms are filled with rare and beautiful treasures.

Proverbs 24:3-4

EXPECTANT MOTHER'S *Journal*

How active is your unborn child?
What patterns of stillness and wakefulness have you noticed?

_____

_____

_____

_____

_____

_____

_____

_____

_____

_____

_____

_____

_____

_____

_____

_____

_____

_____

_____

_____

_____

_____

_____

_____

_____

_____

My frame was not hidden from you when I was made in the secret place.

Psalm 139:15

EXPECTANT MOTHER'S *Journal*

Do you have any concerns about your baby's
wholeness and well-being? What Bible promises can
you take to heart to give you confidence in this area?

_____

_____

_____

_____

_____

_____

_____

_____

_____

_____

_____

_____

_____

_____

_____

_____

_____

_____

_____

_____

_____

Yes, be bold and strong! Banish fear and doubt! For remember, the Lord your
God is with you wherever you go.

Joshua 1:9 TLB

EXPECTANT MOTHER'S *Journal*

Do you have any concerns about labor and delivery?
Will someone be praying for you, your husband, and your baby?

_____

_____

_____

_____

_____

_____

_____

_____

_____

_____

_____

_____

_____

_____

_____

_____

_____

_____

_____

_____

_____

_____

_____

When I am afraid, I will put my confidence in you. Yes, I will trust the promises of God.

Psalm 56:3 TLB

EXPECTANT MOTHER'S *Journal*

What special instructions has your doctor given you for these
last few months? Describe how you feel about these instructions.

He that walketh with wise men shall be wise.

Proverbs 13:20 KJV

EXPECTANT MOTHER'S *Journal*

Are you tired of being pregnant?
Describe your longing to hold your soon-to-be-born child.

_____

_____

_____

_____

_____

_____

_____

_____

_____

_____

_____

_____

_____

_____

_____

_____

_____

_____

_____

_____

_____

_____

_____

_____

You have need of endurance, so that when you have done the will of God, you may receive what was promised.

Hebrews 10:36 NASB

EXPECTANT MOTHER'S *Journal*

Describe your physical body and
how you feel about being so "very pregnant."
Have you chosen an exercise program for the weeks after delivery?

_____

_____

_____

_____

_____

_____

_____

_____

_____

_____

_____

_____

_____

_____

_____

_____

_____

_____

_____

_____

_____

"My grace is sufficient for you, for My strength is made perfect in weakness."

2 Corinthians 12:9 NKJV

EXPECTANT MOTHER'S *Journal*

What final preparations are you making?
Do you have someone to help after you come home from the hospital?

_____

_____

_____

_____

_____

_____

_____

_____

_____

_____

_____

_____

_____

_____

_____

_____

_____

_____

_____

_____

_____

_____

_____

_____

I am sure that God who began the good work within you will keep right on
helping you grow in his grace until his task within you is finally finished.

Philippians 1:6 TLB

EXPECTANT MOTHER'S *Journal*

How well have you been sleeping? What ways have you
found to rest and prepare for the exertion of childbirth?

When you lie down, you will not be afraid; when you lie down, your sleep will be sweet.

Proverbs 3:24

Have you been given a baby shower, or have you received gifts from
friends and family? Describe the gifts and the people who gave them.

All thy children shall be taught of the LORD; and great shall be the peace of thy children.

Isaiah 54:13 KJV

EXPECTANT MOTHER'S *Journal*

What have you learned about yourself during this pregnancy?
What things have made you a stronger person?

_____

_____

_____

_____

_____

_____

_____

_____

_____

_____

_____

_____

_____

_____

_____

_____

_____

_____

_____

_____

_____

_____

It is God that girdeth me with strength, and maketh my way perfect.

Psalm 18:32 KJV

EXPECTANT MOTHER'S *Journal*

How will you draw your husband into
the close circle of mother and child?

_____

_____

_____

_____

_____

_____

_____

_____

_____

_____

_____

_____

_____

_____

_____

_____

_____

_____

_____

_____

_____

_____

_____

_____

Two are better than one; because they have a good reward for their labor.
For if they fall, the one will lift up his fellow.

Ecclesiastes 4:9-10 KJV

EXPECTANT MOTHER'S *Journal*

What parts of your pregnancy were the most difficult for you?
What parts did you enjoy the most?

_____

_____

_____

_____

_____

_____

_____

_____

_____

_____

_____

_____

_____

_____

_____

_____

_____

_____

_____

_____

_____

Women will be preserved through the bearing of children if they continue in faith and love and sanctity with self-restraint.

1 Timothy 2:15 NASB

EXPECTANT MOTHER'S *Journal*

Describe the kind of mother you think you will be.
Describe the kind of mother you hope you will be.

_____

_____

_____

_____

_____

_____

_____

_____

_____

_____

_____

_____

_____

_____

_____

_____

_____

_____

_____

_____

_____

_____

_____

_____

_____

What you decide on will be done, and light will shine on your ways.

Job 22:28

EXPECTANT MOTHER'S *Journal*

How are you preparing your loved ones—
parents, other children, etc.—for the baby's arrival?
What part will you want them to play in the baby's early life?

_____

_____

_____

_____

_____

_____

_____

_____

_____

_____

_____

_____

_____

_____

_____

_____

_____

_____

_____

_____

_____

_____

_____

Behold, children are a gift of the LORD, The fruit of the womb is a reward.

Psalm 127:3 NASB

EXPECTANT MOTHER'S *Journal*

How will you and your family celebrate the birth of this child?
What special keepsakes will you cherish?

_____

_____

_____

_____

_____

_____

_____

_____

_____

_____

_____

_____

_____

_____

_____

_____

_____

_____

_____

_____

_____

_____

_____

_____

Brethren, stand firm and hold to the traditions which you were taught, whether by word of mouth or by letter from us.

2 Thessalonians 2:15 NASB

EXPECTANT MOTHER'S *Journal*

What is your plan for getting to the hospital when the time comes?
Whom will you call right away?

_____

_____

_____

_____

_____

_____

_____

_____

_____

_____

_____

_____

_____

_____

_____

_____

_____

_____

_____

_____

_____

_____

_____

_____

_____

_____

_____

_____

_____

_____

_____

_____

_____

_____

_____

_____

_____

_____

_____

_____

_____

_____

_____

_____

_____

_____

"Be on the alert then, for you do not know the day nor the hour."

Matthew 25:13 NASB

EXPECTANT MOTHER'S *Journal*

Have you experienced any mild contractions?
In what ways is your body preparing for childbirth?

_____

_____

_____

_____

_____

_____

_____

_____

_____

_____

_____

_____

_____

_____

_____

_____

_____

_____

_____

_____

_____

_____

_____

_____

_____

_____

My body is racked with pain, pangs seize me, like those of a woman in labor.

Isaiah 21:3

EXPECTANT MOTHER'S *Journal*

Record your husband's birth weight and your own.
What does your doctor estimate will be the size of your baby?

_____

_____

_____

_____

_____

_____

_____

_____

_____

_____

_____

_____

_____

_____

_____

_____

_____

_____

_____

_____

_____

_____

When I was woven together in the depths of the earth, your eyes saw my unformed body.

Psalms 139:15-16

EXPECTANT MOTHER'S *Journal*

Which of your physical characteristics do you hope your child will receive?
Which of your husband's physical traits?

You created my inmost being; you knit me together in my mother's womb.

Psalm 139:13

EXPECTANT MOTHER'S *Journal*

Describe your emotional condition during these final days of waiting.
Whom are you leaning on most for strength?

God assured us, "I'll never let you down, never walk off and leave you."

Hebrews 13:5 THE MESSAGE

EXPECTANT MOTHER'S *Journal*

What are your doctor's pre-delivery instructions?
How much will your husband be involved?

_____

_____

_____

_____

_____

_____

_____

_____

_____

_____

_____

_____

_____

_____

_____

_____

_____

_____

_____

_____

_____

_____

_____

Wisdom is the principal thing; Therefore get wisdom. And in all your getting, get understanding.

Proverbs 4:7 NKJV

EXPECTANT MOTHER'S *Journal*

Describe your first pangs of labor.
Were they what you expected?

_____

_____

_____

_____

_____

_____

_____

_____

_____

_____

_____

_____

_____

_____

_____

_____

_____

_____

_____

_____

Weeping may remain for a night, but rejoicing comes in the morning.

Psalm 30:5

EXPECTANT MOTHER'S *Journal*

Describe your most difficult hours of labor.
Were they what you expected?

_____

_____

_____

_____

_____

_____

_____

_____

_____

_____

_____

_____

_____

_____

_____

_____

_____

_____

_____

_____

_____

_____

"When a woman is about to give birth, she is in great pain. But after it is all over, she forgets the pain and is happy, because she has brought a child into the world."

John 16:21 CEV

EXPECTANT MOTHER'S *Journal*

Describe what you recall about your delivery.

You must be very careful not to forget the things you have seen God do for you. Keep reminding yourselves, and tell your children and grandchildren as well.

Deuteronomy 4:9 CEV

EXPECTANT MOTHER'S *Journal*

Describe the emotions you felt when
you saw your child for the first time.

With singing lips my mouth will praise you. On my bed I remember you;
I think of you through the watches of the night.

Psalm 63:5-6

EXPECTANT MOTHER'S *Journal*

How did your husband deal with the pain of your labor and delivery?
What was his reaction when he first saw his child?

A man leaves his father and mother and is joined to his wife, and the two are united into one.

Ephesians 5:31 NLT

EXPECTANT MOTHER'S *Journal*

Describe your child from head to toe.
Which characteristics are unique, and which are familiar?

_____

_____

_____

_____

_____

_____

_____

_____

_____

_____

_____

_____

_____

_____

_____

_____

_____

_____

_____

_____

_____

_____

_____

_____

_____

I praise you because I am fearfully and wonderfully made; your works are wonderful, I know that full well.

Psalm 139:14

EXPECTANT MOTHER'S *Journal*

What name have you chosen for your child?
Explain your choice and any special significance the name may hold.

_____

_____

_____

_____

_____

_____

_____

_____

_____

_____

_____

_____

_____

_____

_____

_____

_____

_____

_____

_____

_____

_____

_____

_____

_____

_____

A good name is more desirable than great riches.

Proverbs 22:1

EXPECTANT MOTHER'S *Journal*

How has the experience of giving birth changed you as a woman?
How has it strengthened your relationship with your husband?

_____

_____

_____

_____

_____

_____

_____

_____

_____

_____

_____

_____

_____

_____

_____

_____

_____

_____

_____

_____

_____

_____

_____

_____

_____

_____

We also glory in tribulations, knowing that tribulation produces perseverance; and perseverance, character; and character, hope.

Romans 5:3-4 NKJV

EXPECTANT MOTHER'S *Journal*

How will God be part of your life in the weeks, months, and years ahead?

_____

_____

_____

_____

_____

_____

_____

_____

_____

_____

_____

_____

_____

_____

_____

_____

_____

_____

_____

_____

_____

_____

_____

_____

_____

The work of righteousness will be peace, And the effect of righteousness, quietness and assurance forever.

Isaiah 32:17 NKJV

Additional copies of this journal
and other works by
Angela Thomas Guffey
are available from your local bookstore.

Prayers for Expectant Mothers
Prayers for New Mothers

If you have enjoyed this book, or if it has impacted your life,
we would like to hear from you.

Please contact us at:

Honor Books
4050 Lee Vance View
Colorado Springs, Colorado 80918

Or by e-mail at info@cookministries.org